Acros Curriculum: SCIENCE for ages 7–8

A wide range of teachers' notes and photocopiable worksheets to address the needs of teachers and pupils in covering several aspects of the curriculum, while learning valuable concepts in science.

Across the Curriculum Science for ages 7–8

Contents

Page

Across the Curriculum Science for ages 7–8

Contents

We show possible curriculum links but we will not have thought of everything so you may like to add some of your own.

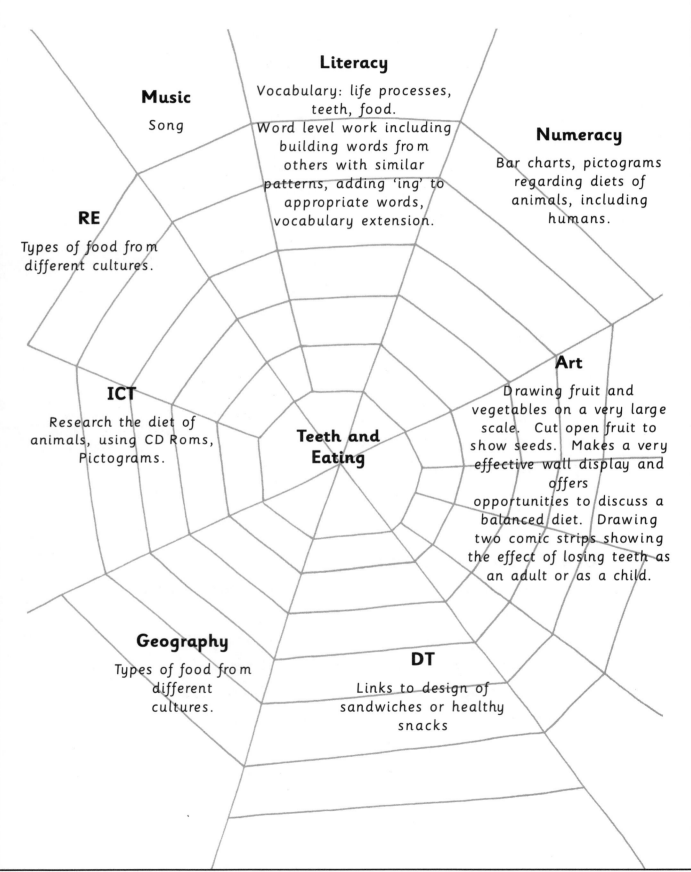

Music

Song

Literacy

Vocabulary: life processes, teeth, food.
Word level work including building words from others with similar patterns, adding 'ing' to appropriate words, vocabulary extension.

Numeracy

Bar charts, pictograms regarding diets of animals, including humans.

RE

Types of food from different cultures.

ICT

Research the diet of animals, using CD Roms, Pictograms.

Teeth and Eating

Art

Drawing fruit and vegetables on a very large scale. Cut open fruit to show seeds. Makes a very effective wall display and offers opportunities to discuss a balanced diet. Drawing two comic strips showing the effect of losing teeth as an adult or as a child.

Geography

Types of food from different cultures.

DT

Links to design of sandwiches or healthy snacks

Worksheet 1 includes vocabulary regarding life processes. Aspects of Year 3 word level work are addressed, including: building words from others with similar patterns; observing the spellings of words when 'ing' is added; vocabulary extension; alphabetical order.

Worksheet 2 includes specific vocabulary for the topic. Valuable discussion can be generated in noting changes in Tim now that he is a toddler, compared to Tim on Worksheet 1.

Worksheet 3 provides some relevant non-fiction reading that covers specific scientific vocabulary.

Worksheet 4 follows the suggestion that children should investigate a question about the diet of animals, specifically the diet of a cat. You may feel that is an impractical task! Accordingly we suggest that you use this page for discussion, to ensure that children understand the pictogram and what it represents, then follow this page with the class investigation provided on Worksheet 5.

Worksheet 5 enables children to create a pictogram of results when investigating the favourite drinks of members of the class.

Worksheet 6 is designed as a discussion sheet, forming an introduction to an art activity. Giant pictures of fruit, created using pastels/chalks on sugar paper, can produce a stunning display for the classroom wall. More importantly the children will need to make close observations — the skill of looking carefully applies equally to science and art.

Worksheets 7 and 8 are used together. The children are provided with the opportunity to sequence two stories and to contrast what happens to an adult with what happens to a child when a tooth comes out. Two pictures are missing, one from each story, and the children are asked to draw these.

Worksheet 9 covers aspects of numeracy and DT. The net of a cuboid is shown, then it is redrawn with tabs. You could ask the children what the tabs are there for to ensure that they understand the need for a method of joining.

Name: Date:

Baby Tim

Use words from the box to fill the gaps in this piece of writing.

WORD BANK

growing	active	health
healthy	activity	energy
energetic	activities	healthily
tooth	teeth	food
fed	feed	feeding	grow
growth		

When Tim was born he had no t_____. He is eight months old now and he still only has one t_____ so he can not chew his f_____ properly. His mum and dad f_____ him with soft food that is easy for him to swallow.

The food helps Tim to g_____ and to keep h_____. It also gives him e_____ to practise walking. Tim is very a_____, crawling and playing with his toys. He gets into lots of mischief!

Find words in the word bank to write in these lists:

Beginning with a: ☐ ☐ ☐

Beginning with e: ☐ ☐

Beginning with f: ☐ ☐ ☐ ☐

Beginning with g: ☐ ☐ ☐

Beginning with h: ☐ ☐ ☐

Beginning with t: ☐ ☐

Name: Date:

Toddler Tim

Tim is a toddler. When he was born he had no teeth. His main food was milk. When he was a baby, his teeth began to grow.

He now has lots of teeth. He has teeth on his upper jaw and on his lower jaw.

Tim uses his front teeth to bite his food. For example, he can bite an apple.

He uses his back teeth to chew his food.

Use these words to label the picture of an adult's mouth:

biting teeth   chewing teeth
upper jaw   lower jaw
tongue   gums

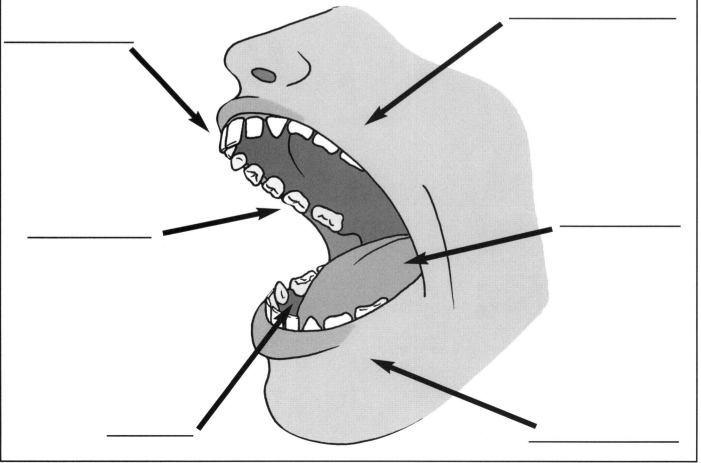

Name: Date:

Teenager Tim

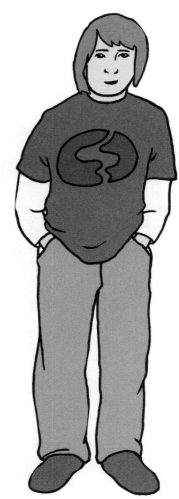

Tim is a teenager. All his baby teeth have gone and his adult teeth have grown.

He has got thirty-two teeth altogether. He has four types of teeth. The four types are called incisors, canines, premolars and molars.

The incisors are at the front of the mouth. They are used for biting and cutting food. They are sharp teeth. The canines are just behind the incisors. They are used for biting and tearing food. They are also sharp teeth.

The premolars are between the canines and the molars. The molars are at the back of the mouth. They are not very sharp but they are wide. The premolars and molars are used for chewing food.

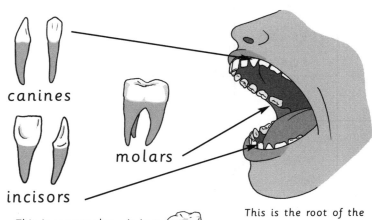

canines

molars

incisors

This is a premolar. It is a similar shape to a molar but it is smaller and the root is different.

This is the root of the tooth. We cannot see the roots in Tim's mouth as they are under the gums.

Unlike Teenager Tim, you have not got all your adult teeth yet.
Use a mirror to look in your mouth.

How many teeth have you got in your lower jaw?

How many teeth have you got in your upper jaw?

How many teeth have you got altogether?

How many incisors have you got?

How many molars have you got?

How many canines have you got?

Name: Date:

What do cats eat?

Miss Devi asked her class about their pet cats.

What is your cat's diet?

My cat eats fish.

My cat eats tinned food.

My cat eats dried food.

My cat eats chicken.

Lots of other children answered the question. They made a pictogram and a bar chart.

chicken

fish

dried food

tinned food

Pictogram showing the diets of cats

number of cats

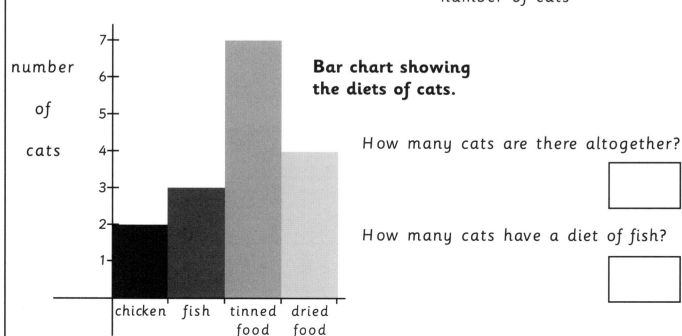

Bar chart showing the diets of cats.

How many cats are there altogether?

How many cats have a diet of fish?

Name: | Date:

Favourite drinks

Here are six drinks. Ask everyone in your class which one is their favourite.

| tea | cola | milk | apple juice | water | lemonade |

☐ ☐ ☐ ☐ ☐ ☐

Draw a pictogram to show your results. Draw a stick person to represent every child.

tea

cola

milk

apple juice

water

lemonade

Which drinks could be bad for teeth? Do you know why?

Which drinks will not harm teeth?

Which is the most popular drink? Is it bad for teeth?

Andrew Brodie Publications © A & C Black Publishers Ltd.

Name: Date:

Seeds

Can you identify these fruits?
Can you see the seeds?

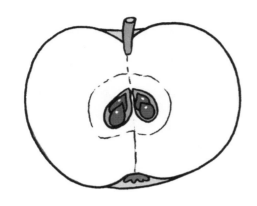

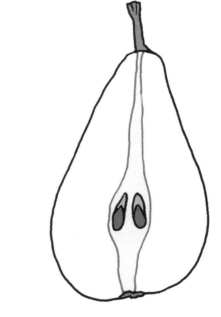

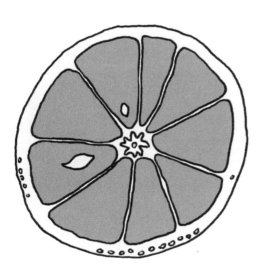

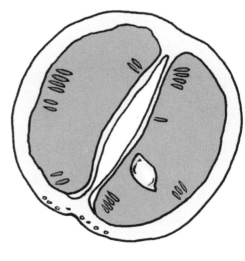

Look carefully at some fruit.
Choose one piece of fruit to draw.

Make a **really big** drawing to go on the wall.

Name:

Date:

When a tooth falls out

Cut out the pictures on Worksheet 8 and stick them in the right places. One picture is missing from each story. Draw the missing picture.

Tanny is eight years old.

One of her milk teeth comes out.

She puts it under her pillow.

Soon a new tooth grows.

She cleans her teeth every day.

She has good teeth.

Mrs Jones is forty-eight years old.

She has toothache.

She goes to the dentist.

The dentist says the tooth must come out.

Mrs Jones has a gap.

She has to have a false tooth.

Name: Date:

When a tooth falls out

Pictures for Worksheet 7

 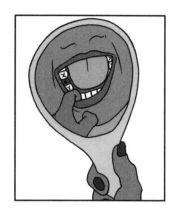 

  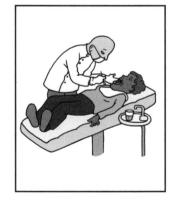

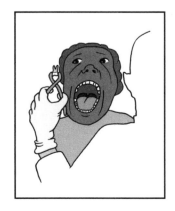

Numeracy/DT

Name: Date:

Design a box

Here is the net of a cuboid.

Design a box for healthy, sugar-free sweets.

It should look attractive.

It should have writing that persuades children to eat healthily.

Andrew Brodie Publications © A & C Black Publishers Ltd.

We show possible curriculum links but we will not have thought of everything so you may like to add some of your own.

Music

Make up a song for Reception, using a repeating pattern. For example, based on ten green bottles, five green cabbages growing in the garden.

Literacy

Words to describe physical characteristics of plants: e.g. colours, pale, thin, spindly. Expressions of reason using 'because'. Expressions of generalisations.

ICT

Use a digital camera to record growth of plants on a daily basis.

RE

Prayer of thanks for plants that grow and food we eat. Parable of the sower.

Art

Making a poster: what we need to make plants grow:
  – sunlight
  – water
  – nutrients in the soil
  – temperature
– healthy leaves/roots/stems
Observational drawings: comparing and contrasting healthy and unhealthy plants.

Helping Plants Grow Well

Geography

Visit a local supermarket or greengrocer:
List five fruits, five vegetables.
two vegetables where the root is eaten.
two vegetables where the leaves are eaten.
two fruits that grow on trees.
two vegetables you've never tried.

Numeracy

Careful measuring: heights of plants, volumes of water – standard measures. Fair testing. Temperature.

Worksheet 1 covers a vast range of vocabulary. Some of this is specifically related to plants but much of the vocabulary is used more widely on a day-to-day basis. The children are encouraged to examine their plants closely then report on what they find. This report could be spoken or written, or both. If you ask the children to describe the plant in writing they could use the writing frame on Worksheet 2.

Worksheet 3 provides opportunities for measurement and use of IT. Geraniums are a good choice of plant for this activity. You may wish the children to write about what they observe – this provides a meaningful opportunity for written work. The measurements that children take can be recorded on Worksheet 4. We have included a picture of a ruler to allow for discussion regarding taking appropriate measurements. Perhaps surprisingly, experience has taught us that some children will look more carefully at a picture of a ruler than at the ruler itself, but will then be able to use the real ruler applying what they have learnt from the picture! We suggest that you discuss the length of the black line with the children. This will help to establish how accurate they are at measuring using standard units. You may decide that they should measure to the nearest centimetre or, if they are competent at measuring, to the nearest millimetre.

Worksheet 5 concerns a visit to a supermarket or greengrocer and can contribute to children's knowledge and understanding of their own locality.

Worksheet 6 gives ideas for a poster but the design itself is created by each child. They should be encouraged to consider a poster as a means of giving information, not just as a pretty picture. Accordingly they should incorporate appropriate wording to give clear explanations regarding what a plant needs to ensure it grows well. Worksheet 7 continues this core concept.

Worksheet 8 could be used at harvest time, though its message is always relevant.

| Name: | Date: |

Describing a plant

Your teacher has provided you with a plant in a pot. Look very carefully at it.

Look closely at the leaves. Are they green all over? Do they have any yellow or red on them?

How many leaves are there?

Look at the stem. Is it thick or spindly?

Look at the soil. Can you see any roots or are they completely in the soil?

How tall is your plant?

Use some of these words to describe your plant.

colours	**shades**	**numbers**	
green	pale	one	two
yellow	dark	three	four
red		five	six
brown		seven	eight
black	**plant words**	nine	ten
pink		eleven	twelve
	stem	thirteen	fourteen
	leaf	fifteen	sixteen
	flower	seventeen	eighteen
	roots	nineteen	twenty
	pot		
	soil		

other words

straight
bent
thick
thin
spindly
strong
weak

measuring

centimetres
roughly
about
approximately

HELPING PLANTS GROW WELL

Literacy/Art

Name: Date:

Your plant

Draw your plant very carefully.

Describe your plant very carefully.

Name: Date:

Do plants need leaves?

Experiment: To find out if plants need leaves to grow well.

1 You will need two plants that are the same species.

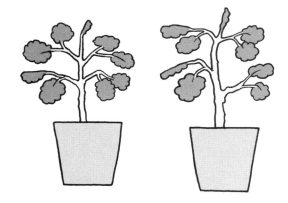

2 Remove most of the leaves from one plant.

3 Use a ruler to measure the height of the plants from the top of the soil to the top of the plant. Write the measurement in the chart on Worksheet 4.

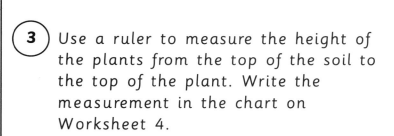

4 Use a digital camera to take a picture of both plants.

5 Put the plants in the same place and water them carefully.

6 Measure the plants every day and take a photograph to show the changes.

You may find that both plants grow more leaves. Do not remove any of these.

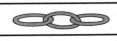
Name: Date:

Do plants need leaves?

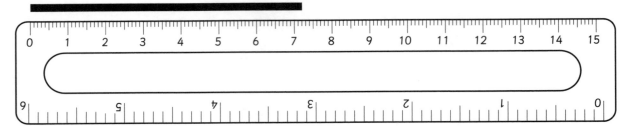

You will need a longer ruler to measure your plants.

Fill in this chart every day.

	Height of plant 1	Height of plant 2	Number of leaves on plant 1	Number of leaves on plant 2
Day 1				
Day 2				
Day 3				
Day 4				
Day 5				
Day 6				
Day 7				
Day 8				
Day 9				
Day 10				
Day 11				
Day 12				
Day 13				
Day 14				

What do you notice? _____

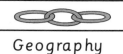
Name: | **Date:**

Plants provide food

We eat different parts of plants.

  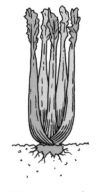 

We eat the root of a carrot plant.

We eat the leaves of a lettuce.

We eat the stems of celery.

We eat the fruit of an apple tree.

Visit a local supermarket or greengrocer and fill in this chart.

Two vegetables of which you eat the root.		
Two vegetables of which you eat the leaves.		
Two fruits that grow on trees.		
Two fruits that you have never tried.		
Two vegetables that you have never tried.		

Did you know a tomato is a fruit? It is because a fruit contains seeds.

Name: Date:

Design a poster

Design a poster to go on your classroom wall.
The poster should explain what a plant
needs to grow well.

Draw a plant in a pot.

Remember to show all the things a plant needs.

Remember to use some labels.   You may need to write some explanations as
well. Below are some words you could use. Practise spelling them.

plant	_____	sunlight	_____
stem	_____	warmth	_____
leaf	_____	temperature	_____
roots	_____	green	_____
pot	_____	yellow	_____
soil	_____	tall	_____
water	_____	centimetres	_____
strong	_____	healthy	_____

| Name: | Date: |

What a plant needs

You have observed plants growing and you know what they need to grow well. Put a tick by the correct statement in each line below:

Plants grow well when they have:

1 sunlight ☐ darkness ☐

2 lots of water ☐ some water ☐ no water ☐

3 cold temperatures ☐ hot temperatures ☐ warm temperatures ☐

4 soil ☐ sand ☐ just water ☐

Using the tune of 'Ten Green Bottles', make up a song to sing to the Reception class. Your song should explain to them the conditions that plants need to help them to grow well.

Name: _____ Date: _____

Foods we eat

Write the names of three vegetables we eat.

_____ _____ _____

Write the names of three fruits we eat.

_____ _____ _____

Unscramble the letters to find the names of some grain that we eat. The first one is done for you.

eric ➡ rice

tweha ➡ ☐☐☐☐☐

ronc ➡ ☐☐☐☐

labyre ➡ ☐☐☐☐☐☐

sota ➡ ☐☐☐☐

Fruit, vegetables and grain are all very important foods. We need them to grow well.
Write a prayer of thanks for the foods that we eat.

_____

_____

_____

_____

_____

_____

_____

_____

We show possible curriculum links but we will not have thought of everything so you may like to add some of your own.

Literacy
Words to describe physical characteristics, e.g. strong, hard, flexible, absorbent, transparent, rigid, opaque, weak, smooth, etc.
Investigative words, e.g, describe, description, test, explain, compare, investigate, conclude, evidence, etc.

PE
Different balls are made of different materials. Children could test how far they can throw a cricket ball/rounders ball/tennis ball/windball/ rubber ball. Which material is easiest to throw? Does the material affect the distance thrown?

ICT
Making a database based on properties of materials.

Art
Drawing buildings, observing how different materials have been used together.

History
Could consider different materials that have been used over time for the same items, e.g, buckets, bridges, wheels.

Music
Different materials create different sounds, e.g, glockenspiel, xylophone.

Characteristics of Materials

Geography
A walk in the locality to observe the different uses of materials.

DT
Investigation: Do the characteristics of a piece of paper change when you roll it or fold it?

Numeracy
Measurements of length. Creating a table of properties of materials related to their characteristics. Measurements of small volumes of water when testing materials for absorbency.

Worksheet 1 includes work on opposites, using some of the key vocabulary related to characteristics of materials.

Worksheet 2 covers scientific vocabulary that may be used by the children when writing explanations for their findings from the investigations completed within this unit.

Worksheet 3 features a simple investigation. The children will probably discover that it is only possible to make a total of eight folds of a single piece of paper, whatever size the paper is and whatever type of paper it is.

Worksheet 4 presents a second investigation. This could be a challenge for the whole class: who can make the tallest tower? A table of results could be created when everyone has finished building and measuring their towers. Each completed tower should be examined to try to establish why it did or didn't succeed in its purpose of achieving height.

Worksheet 6 – The children could put ticks on their chart before the walk to predict what they will see, then use a different colour or cross the tick when they are actually on the walk. When you return from the walk you could choose one of the structures and explain why it is made of those particular materials.

Worksheet 7 – Children often draw 'standard' homes. Close observation of the construction materials will help observational skills.

Worksheet 8 – Drawing tables to show data is a key skill in numeracy. On this page we give children the attributes to consider when drawing their own table. This work would also be ideally suited to ICT – children could create their own researchable database.

Name: Date:

Opposites

These are some words that we can use to describe materials.

WORD BANK

rigid   hard   opaque

smooth   weak   dull

Find words in the word bank ...

...that are the opposites of the words below.

soft   ➡️ [ ]

flexible   ➡️ [ ]

shiny   ➡️ [ ]

rough   ➡️ [ ]

transparent   ➡️ [ ]

strong   ➡️ [ ]

Find some things in the room that can be written in these lists.
Some things can be put in more than one list.

soft things	shiny things	smooth things
_____	_____	_____
_____	_____	_____
_____	_____	_____
_____	_____	_____
_____	_____	_____
_____	_____	_____

CHARACTERISTICS OF MATERIALS

Literacy

Name: _____ Date: _____

Scientific words

You are going to carry out some investigations using sheets of paper.

When you have completed your experiments you need to write about them.

In the wordsearch are some of the words you will need when you write about your investigations.

Try to find one word from each of these pairs of words:

test	~	testing	investigate	~	investigation
experiment	~	experimenting	describe	~	description
explain	~	explanation	conclude	~	conclusion
fair	~	unfair	compare	~	comparing

c	q	a	i	n	v	e	s	t	i	g	a	t	e	s	z
o	c	u	j	l	b	e	a	k	x	p	i	r	x	m	o
n	p	c	y	f	h	m	k	p	n	w	q	e	p	p	n
c	o	m	p	a	r	i	n	g	e	i	z	p	l	t	q
l	i	w	h	i	g	l	n	t	t	h	m	o	a	a	m
u	a	k	b	r	s	l	m	d	e	s	c	r	i	b	e
d	w	t	p	e	r	p	g	f	s	j	s	y	n	s	r
e	x	p	e	r	i	m	e	n	t	f	d	l	m	x	c

Now write the words from the pairs that were not in the wordsearch.

_____ _____ _____

_____ _____ _____

_____ _____

Name: **Date:**

Folding paper

All you need is a flat piece of paper.

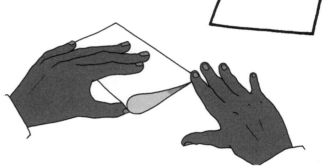

(**1**) Fold the paper in half.

(**2**) Fold the paper in half again.

(**3**) Keep folding the paper, until you can't fold anymore. Count the number of folds you make.

How many folds did you make? ☐

What do you predict will happen if you use a bigger piece of paper?

_____

_____

What do you predict will happen if you use a thinner piece of paper?

_____

_____

Try the investigation again, with different paper. Write down what you find out.

_____

_____

_____

Name: **Date:**

Investigation

Who can make the tallest tower that doesn't fall over?

You are allowed to use six sheets of newspaper and twelve pieces of sticky tape.

Remember: paper can be folded

paper can be rolled

paper can be screwed up

You have fifteen minutes to work with a partner to make a tower.

At the end of the time you must measure the height of your tower in centimetres.

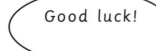

Good luck!

Name: **Date:**

Buildings and structures

You are going for a walk near your school.

Make sure you stay near an adult. They need you to look after them.

You are going to look for man-made buildings and structures. You will probably see trees and other plants but they are not man-made.

You may see:
- bridges
- houses
- lampposts
- telegraph poles
- road signs
- railway lines
- shops
- farms
- barns
- factories
- fences

GIVE WAY

Remember the safety rules:

Do not go anywhere alone, stay with friends.

Keep near one of the adults who are with you on the walk.

Do not go onto private property.

Don't run or talk when crossing roads. Keep looking and listening.

Follow your teacher's instructions at all times.

Name: | Date:

Structures and materials

Tick boxes in this chart to show what you see on the walk.

Remember, some structures will be made of more than one material.

Material

Structure	Wood	Metal	Glass	Plastic	Brick	Stone	Concrete	Other
House								
Bridge								
Fence								
Lamppost								
Telegraph post								
Road sign								
Railway lines								
Shops								
Farms								
Barns								
Factories								

Name: Date:

What is a house made of?

Look carefully at a house, and all the materials you can see on it.

WORD BANK

stone   brick   slate

concrete   wood   plastic

glass   metal

Look at the roof, the walls, the television aerial, the doors, the windows, the guttering, the drain-pipes. Look at everything.

Draw the house here.
Draw neat arrows to parts of the building.
Write what each part is made from.

CHARACTERISTICS OF MATERIALS

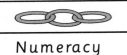

Numeracy

Name: Date:

What are materials like?

Here is a list of materials. You may be able to think of more.

Here is a list of characteristics. You may be able to think of more.

wood	soft
metal	hard
plastic	shiny
glass	transparent
stone	brittle
wool	opaque
concrete	fragile
	strong

Draw a chart to relate the materials to their characteristics. Put ticks in the correct boxes on your chart.

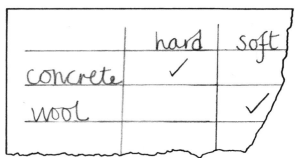

We show possible curriculum links but we will not have thought of everything so you may like to add some of your own.

Literacy

Extension of vocabulary. Development of speaking and history skills. Reading information texts.

PE

ICT

Introduction to databases. (Sorting and recording details from rock samples.)

RE

Use of stone in religious buildings.

Art

Sculpture to improve environment (based on rock sculptures and modelling in sand/clay).

History

Local work links to land use, local stone. Ancient Egypt, pyramids, temples. Anglo-Saxon – work to do with archaeological digs.

Rocks and Soils

DT

Making a display container for rock samples.

Geography

Link to local investigation with types of local stone/soil.

Numeracy

Word problems. Using standard measures (weighing, etc.).

Worksheets 1 and 2 include a useful range of vocabulary related to the scientific study of rocks and soils. These Worksheets provide opportunities for relevant non-fiction reading.

Worksheets 3 and 4 provide numeracy work linked to the subject of rocks and soils. On any visits related to this topic children may well come across display units such as this one. For investigations 1 and 2 children will need to write in a notebook or on a separate piece of paper.

Worksheet 5 is intended for class/group discussion via photocopying onto OHP or for each pair/group of children to read and work from. This activity is best done by the children in pairs or groups of three. The task is intended for use instead of the similar QCA Year 3 design units concerning structures. (Packaging/Photo frames).
– It is important that the children are either familiar with 'nets' of basic shapes or have the opportunity to examine cardboard containers to note tabs/flaps, etc.
– Ensure the rock samples are small and light.
– In the event of sufficient rock samples being unavailable marbles would be an acceptable substitute to ensure each pair/group had 'samples' to work with.
– Encourage sections within display container.
– Encourage labelling of sections for types of rock.
Suggested materials – varying thicknesses and types of card, sticky tape, glue, etc., clear acetate or similar (to allow clear lids to be made), any other suitable materials available in the classroom.
Extension – the suggestion of a folding stand on the base of their display container could be introduced (such as you might find on a photo frame).

Worksheet 6 is suitable for individual/group work or for use with OHP.
The Worksheet is very much a 'starting point' rather than a complete detailed task. The reason for this is that the activities very much depend on the rock samples used.

Worksheet 7 builds on children's previous understanding of using natural materials and will reinforce/develop their understanding of the characteristics of types of rock.
Materials needed – sand, modelling clay, selection of pictures (holiday brochures are a good source) to include sculpting/decorating of rock: stone in decorative buildings, e.g. rose-red city of Petra (Jordan), Taj Mahal (India), Terracotta Army (China), pyramids/temples (Egypt); naturally occurring rock formations, e.g. Grand Canyon (N. America), Uluru (Ayers Rock, Australia), Wave Rock (Australia).
Discuss which are shaped by man and which are natural formations.
Discuss reasons for use of stone as decoration/building material (aesthetic improvement of environment/long lasting quality of material/local availability).
Discuss use of stone for building/decoration of religious buildings.
Design a sculpture to improve local village, play area, town centre, etc.
Note: Space is given on the photocopiable/OHP sheet for you to insert the destination of your choice.
If some or all children use sand for their mini sculpture you may wish to photograph this due to the short life of the model.

Name: Date:

Find the rocks

Read the words in the rock.
Find them in the wordsearch. They might be written horizontally →,
vertically ↓ or diagonally ↙ ↘. <u>Lightly colour</u> the words as you find them.

boulder   geology   pebble
marble   limestone   chalk
beach   granite   soil   sand
geologist   slate   rock
mountain   stone

g	e	o	l	o	g	y	b	p	x	m	r	o	c	k	x	i	b	e	b	c	v	z	e	v	c
b	x	s	j	q	e	v	o	k	f	o	k	q	f	l	i	v	x	s	l	a	t	e	n	z	h
k	g	v	t	x	o	z	s	v	x	u	z	t	k	v	k	l	q	o	z	k	n	v	b	x	a
e	z	r	q	j	l	s	q	k	j	n	b	w	z	x	v	i	e	q	m	j	j	r	b	z	l
q	e	b	a	q	o	q	u	b	s	t	o	n	e	s	x	m	q	e	k	a	q	v	d	x	k
b	j	t	k	n	g	j	q	o	v	a	b	x	m	z	b	e	j	k	a	q	r	j	j	k	j
b	v	b	q	z	i	x	b	b	b	i	j	k	q	k	z	s	b	x	j	b	b	b	b	j	v
e	b	j	t	j	s	t	h	q	e	n	x	z	f	v	b	t	i	b	r	s	o	i	l	z	s
t	q	x	t	v	t	v	e	b	o	u	l	d	e	r	v	o	o	b	o	a	b	b	l	e	s
t	h	x	z	q	o	u	b	j	k	v	s	v	j	v	a	n	z	n	j	n	z	d	x	s	z
x	o	f	b	b	z	y	e	x	k	z	j	z	a	x	z	e	v	r	q	d	k	v	k	x	s
p	e	b	b	l	e	j	a	q	q	b	e	a	c	h	x	b	x	j	b	q	q	g	v	j	o

Have you found all 15 words?

Now colour all these letters – b j k q v x z.

The remaining letters will spell a message. Find the message by reading each line from left to right. Begin with the top line.

_ _ _ _ _ _ _   _ _   _ _ _ _ _

_ _ _ _ _ _   _ _ _ _   _ _ _ _   _ _

_ _ _   k _ _   _ _ _   _ _ _ _ _   _ _ _ _ _

_ _ _ _ _ _ _ _   _ _   _ _ _ _ _ _

_ _ _ _ .

Name: Date:

Find the rocks

Read the words in the box.
Put the correct word beneath the clue.

WORD BANK

beach   sand   chalk

granite   pebble

slate   geologist   soil

boulder

Rock grains found in a desert or on a beach.

_ _ _ _ _ _

This is made from rock particles, humus, water and air.

_ _ _ _ _

This type of rock can be split into thin layers. It is sometimes used to make roof tiles.

_ _ _ _ _ _

A person who studies rocks.

_ _ _ _ _ _ _ _ _

A soft white rock.

_ _ _ _ _

An area of sand or shingle by the water's edge.

_ _ _ _ _

A smooth rounded stone.

_ _ _ _ _ _

A very hard type of rock, often used for building work.

_ _ _ _ _ _ _

A large chunk of rock.

_ _ _ _ _ _ _

Name: Date:

Rocky problems

Kenrick collects small polished stones to make jewellery.
He buys them from a shop selling rocks and minerals.
Here are some of the stones sold in the shop.

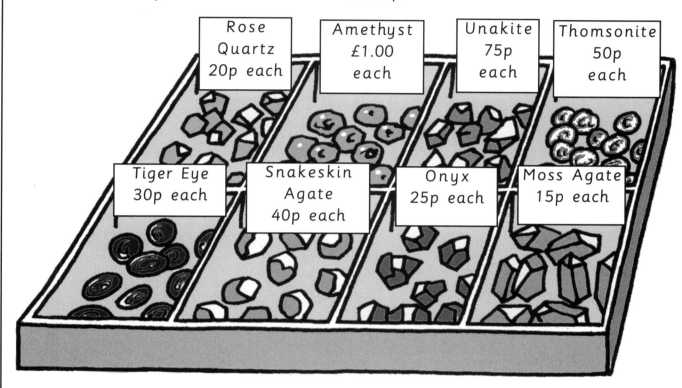

Rose Quartz 20p each

Amethyst £1.00 each

Unakite 75p each

Thomsonite 50p each

Tiger Eye 30p each

Snakeskin Agate 40p each

Onyx 25p each

Moss Agate 15p each

Complete the following:

Kenrick buys 2 pieces of rose quartz.

Total cost =

He buys 4 pieces of onyx.

Total cost =

He buys 3 pieces of moss agate.

Total cost =

He buys 4 tiger eye stones.

Total cost =

Now try the problems on Worksheet 4.

Name: | Date:

Rocky problems

Complete the following:

Kenrick buys 2 pieces of rose quartz and 3 pieces of moss agate.

Total cost = ☐   Change from £1 = ☐

He buys 2 amethysts and a piece of onyx.

Total cost = ☐   Change from £2.50 = ☐

He buys a tiger-eye, a snakeskin agate and a unakite.

Total cost = ☐   Change from £2 = ☐

He buys one of each type of stone.

Total cost of the eight stones = ☐

His change from £4 = ☐

Investigation 1
Kenrick goes to the shop with £1.
Investigate the different ways he could spend **all** of it.

Here is one way to start you off.

4 pieces of onyx (4 x 25p) = £1

Investigation 2
Kenrick was given two different stones.
Work out the cost of each possible pair of stones. (There are 28 possible pairs!)
e.g. rose quartz + unakite = 20p + 75p = 95p
Feeling brainy today?
If so, work out the change from £2 that Kenrick would have after buying each pair of stones.

Name: Date:

Displaying rock samples

You have six small rock samples to display.

Use the materials provided to make a container in which they can be displayed.

It would be ideal if the container could also be used to store them in.

Things to think about!

- Your rock samples could be labelled so that people know what types they are.

- Could you make a clear lid for your container so that it can be used for storage <u>and</u> display?

- Always use cutting tools with care.

- Remember that the flat shape (or net) from which you make your display container needs tabs to enable you to stick it together easily.

- It may help you to use paper-clips to hold pieces together while glue is drying.

- Think about the size of your container.

- Can you make sure your rocks don't rattle about or bump into each other?

Have fun!

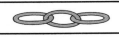
Name: | Date:

Collecting data

Use the computer as much as possible to do this work.

You have been given a selection of pieces of rock.

● Weigh each one and record its weight.

● Look at the colour of the rocks.
Record their colours – name one colour only for each rock (the colour you can see most of in that rock).

● Look for other ways of sorting your pieces of rock, perhaps by shape or texture.
You may have other good ideas.

● Make a bar chart based on the colour of your rocks.

● What other graphs can you make with the information you have?

● You could create your bar charts on the computer.

Name: Date:

Be a sculptor

For thousands of years people have carved shapes from rock.
Look at the pictures you have been given. Which of these have been shaped or built by people?
Why do you think people have sculptured in stone?

Task

● You are going to design a sculpture to improve the _____ .

● First think of some good ideas and discuss your ideas with a friend.

● Sketch your ideas and think about how to make your sketch into a model.

● When you have completed your design you will try making your model from sand or modelling clay.

● Your model will be a small version (maquette) that shows what the real thing might look like.

Important points

● Use modelling tools carefully and safely.

● Your sand <u>must not</u> be too dry or it will not hold together. It <u>must not</u> be too wet or it will not keep its shape. <u>Your sand must be damp!</u>

● You may be given the chance to photograph your model.

Test your knowledge

● If the 'real thing' was to be made, what type of local stone would be the best to use?

–

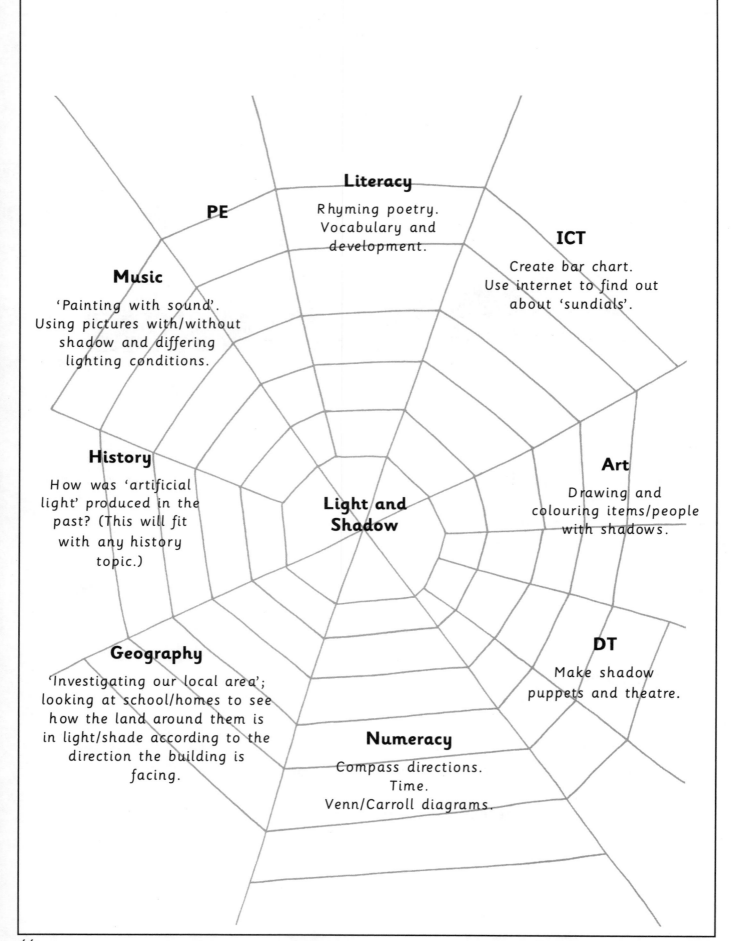

Literacy

Rhyming poetry.
Vocabulary and
development.

PE

ICT

Create bar chart.
Use internet to find out
about 'sundials'.

Music

'Painting with sound'.
Using pictures with/without
shadow and differing
lighting conditions.

History

How was 'artificial
light' produced in the
past? (This will fit
with any history
topic.)

**Light and
Shadow**

Art

Drawing and
colouring items/people
with shadows.

Geography

'Investigating our local area';
looking at school/homes to see
how the land around them is
in light/shade according to the
direction the building is
facing.

DT

Make shadow
puppets and theatre.

Numeracy

Compass directions.
Time.
Venn/Carroll diagrams.

Worksheets 1 and 2 contain a direct literacy activity that is perfectly matched to the science topic on light and shadows. This is through using the Robert Louis Stevenson poem, 'My Shadow'. Children could follow this by writing their own poem or story with the same title.

Worksheets 3, 4 and 5 focus on compass points. Some children will need reminding that the sun rises in the east and sets in the west. The task also deals with using standard measures. The additional activities include calculating distances and understanding right angles.

Worksheet 6 provides simple instructions for some games activities that involve shadows. The instructions include recommended distances but these could be altered according to the agility and coordination of players.

Worksheet 7 is a recording sheet for a very important activity in which children can learn about the movement of the sun. Many of them will be very surprised at their findings.

Worksheet 8 – This work complements QCA Unit 3A ('Portraying Relationships'). It may be useful for children to draw and shade simple objects that are casting a shadow before trying to draw people.
Children should also be given the opportunity to see sketches/paintings/photographs that show figures casting shadows.

Worksheet 9 features a Venn diagram activity for individual or small group use. For frequent use you may wish to copy the sheet onto card or laminate the copy. The elements on the sheet are designed to be cut out by the children. The children decide on correct positioning of all items. (If done individually this could be stuck onto a Venn diagram on A3 paper). This activity could promote much discussion. Areas of potential discussion include:

Light source   Light reflector

    (i) whether a lamp is a light source when it is switched off;
    (ii) whether the moon is a light source as, in fact, it purely reflects the light of the sun.

Music – Although we have not included a Worksheet for this purpose, the science topic 'Light and Shadows' lends itself to the QCA Music unit, 'Painting with Sound'. Children can be given photographs of the same place – preferably in the locality of the school – in different conditions, for example dark stormy day, bright sunny day, early morning, night-time.
In groups they can choose from a range of available classroom instruments, to create a 'sound picture' that matches the mood of the photograph the group has been given. (Only give one photograph to each group.)
The class can then discuss reasons for the choices made for different conditions.

Name: Date:

My Shadow

This poem was written by Robert Louis Stevenson.

I have a little shadow that goes in and out with me,
And what can be the use of him is more than I can see.
He is very, very like me from the heels up to the head;
And I see him jump before me, when I jump into my bed.

The funniest thing about him is the way he likes to grow,
Not at all like proper children, which is always very slow;
For he sometimes shoots up taller like an indiarubber ball,
And he sometimes gets so little that there's none of him at all.

He hasn't got a notion of how children ought to play,
And can only make a fool of me in every sort of way.
He stays so close besides me, he's a coward you can see;
I'd think shame to stick to nursie as that shadow sticks to me!

One morning, very early, before the sun was up,
I rose and found the shining dew on every buttercup;
But my lazy little shadow, like an arrant sleepy-head,
Had stayed at home behind me and was fast asleep in bed.

Name: **Date:**

My Shadow

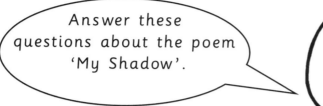 

Answer these questions about the poem 'My Shadow'.

<u>Ring the correct answers.</u>

● How many verses are there in the poem?

one   two   three   four   five   six

● How many lines are in each verse?

one   two   three   four   five   six

● Ring the word used in the poem to rhyme with **bed**.

red   said   shred   fled   head

● Ring the word used in the poem to rhyme with **grow**.

now   slop   toe   slow   mow

<u>Write the answers.</u>

● Write the two pairs of rhyming words used twice in the poem.

_____   _____

● Why does the shadow always 'stay close beside' the child in the poem?

_____

_____

● How does the poem tell us that the child in the poem is a boy?

_____

● Explain why, in the fourth verse, the shadow seems to have 'stayed in bed'.

_____

_____

LIGHT AND SHADOWS

Numeracy

Name: Date:

My day out (Compass points)

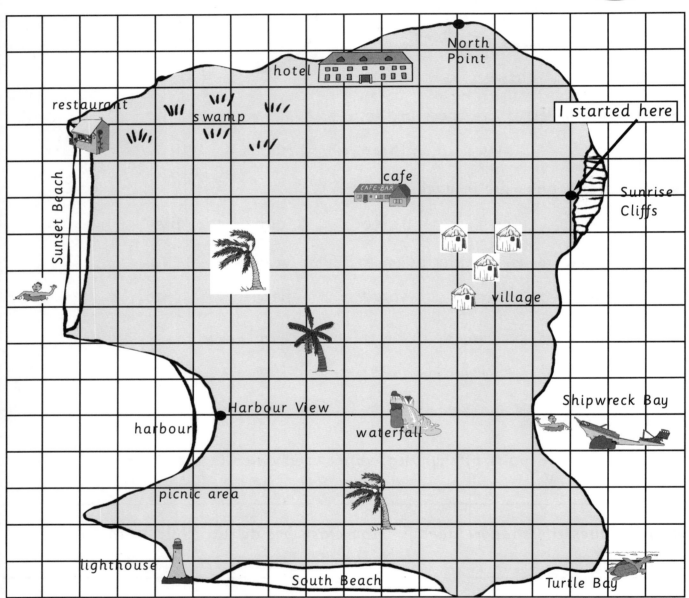

scale = 1 centimetre = 1 kilometre

- Read and complete Worksheets 4 and 5 to find out exactly where I went on my day out.

- As you work you can draw my route on the map.
  Do this carefully using a ruler and a coloured pencil or pen.

Name: **Date:**

My day out

- Use the words <u>north</u>, <u>south</u>, <u>east</u> or <u>west</u> to complete the text.

- Mark the route on the map.

- The completed route should have only horizontal and vertical lines.

My day began when I looked to the _____ from the Sunrise Cliffs to watch the sun come up over the horizon. After this I walked 5 kilometres_____ to have breakfast at the cafe.

Next, I walked 6 kilometres _____, past the village to the waterfall. Here I turned and went 4 kilometres _____ to Shipwreck Bay where I had a swim.

Feeling refreshed I walked the 4 kilometres _____ to Turtle Bay. (I was disappointed not to see any turtles here!)

My next stop was the lighthouse, which I reached after walking _____ for 9 kilometres. Two kilometres _____ from here brought me to the picnic area (lunch at last).

From Worksheet 5 find out where I went after lunch.

Name: _____ Date: _____

My day out

In the warm afternoon sunshine I went 1 kilometre _____ , 5 kilometres _____ and 4 kilometres _____ around the harbour to the southern end of Sunset Beach.

Here I met a friend. We had a swim and then walked along the entire 5 kilometres of the beach. Here we found a restaurant to have dinner while watching the sun setting in the _____ .

I said goodbye to my friend and walked the 7 kilometres _____ and 2 kilometres _____ to reach my hotel without falling into the swamp. I had had a lovely day – but now I was exhausted and my feet ached, so I had a bath and went straight to bed.

Extension activities

● Now mark all the right angles on the route and count them. How many have you found? _____

● Now look at the route and work out how far I walked during the day.
_____ (No wonder my feet ached!)

● What is the distance from:

    ○ North Point to South Beach?   _____

    ○ the waterfall to Harbour View?   _____

    ○ Sunrise Cliffs to the beach restaurant? _____

Name: | Date:

Games Activities (for Sunny Days!)

Read the instructions to learn how to play two games in PE.

1). <u>Shadow in the Middle</u>

Work in groups of three. Each group needs one ball.
Two players stand approximately six metres apart.
The third player stands between the two others.
No player may move more than five steps in any direction.
The outside players must <u>bounce</u> the ball from one to the other, aiming for the bounce to land on the **shadow** of the middle player.
If an outside player succeeds in hitting the shadow, the middle player must change positions with the outside player.

2). <u>Mark the shadow</u>

(Again three children and one ball.)
one child = player   one child = marker   one child = score keeper
The player stands in front of the marker (facing the same direction).
The player must move no more than five steps before changing direction.
(The marker must try to keep facing the same direction as the player).
The marker gains 1 point for each time he/she steps on the 'shadow head' of the player. (The score keeper counts the points gained by the marker).
After two minutes change positions: the marker becomes the player, the player becomes the score keeper, the score keeper becomes the marker.
After two more minutes change again so that each child has taken each position.

Name: Date:

Shadows

- Set up a vertical stick (e.g. a metre stick) on a sunny day.

- Every hour record the length and direction of the shadow on the chart below.

Time	Time	Time
Shadow length	Shadow length	Shadow length
Shadow direction	Shadow direction	Shadow direction
Time	Time	Time
Shadow length	Shadow length	Shadow length
Shadow direction	Shadow direction	Shadow direction

- What did you notice about the length of the shadow during the day?

_____

_____

_____

- What did you notice about the direction of the shadow during the day?

_____

_____

_____

Make a bar chart about the length of the shadow.
You could do this on the computer.

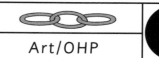
Name: | Date:

Pictures on a sunny day

Do this work after looking at pictures showing the effect of shadows.

- Work with a partner.

- One person is the sitter (or model) and the other the artist.

- The sitter should be in a pose that is easy to stay in for 20 – 30 minutes (so don't try balancing on one leg!).

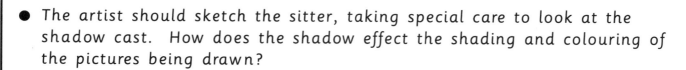

- The artist should sketch the sitter, taking special care to look at the shadow cast. How does the shadow effect the shading and colouring of the pictures being drawn?

- Later on the same day <u>or</u> at a different time on another sunny day, do the same thing again, but this time the sitter and the artist should swap roles. This should be done in the same place.

- Discuss the main differences between the pictures drawn at different times of the day.

<u>Points to note</u>

- Make sure the sitter is <u>not</u> looking directly into the sun.

- The sitter may need sun protection in warm weather.

- If your sketch is to be coloured it is important to see how the colouring is changed in shadowy areas.

- If you are going to use paints for your finished picture, think about how to make paints lighter or darker to show shade.

Venn diagram

Light source

Light reflector

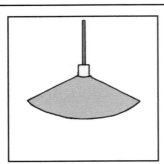

torch

light

flowers

moon

sun

mirror

moon and stars

eyes

fire

sun and water

chair

water

lamp

mirror and lamp

tree

stars

We show possible curriculum links but we will not have thought of everything so you may like to add some of your own.

Literacy

Following written instructions to make spring animals. Technical vocabulary appropriate to magnets and springs.

History

Vikings first to use magnets in navigation.

DT

Making animals with springs. Designing and making pet carrier for spring animal.

Magnets and Springs

Geography

Examples of magnets and springs in local area – school/home.

Numeracy

Measuring – standard units 'cm' for distance of spring's pull.

Worksheet 1 provides a meaningful literacy task of following instructions for gymnastic activities. The suggested activities here can be incorporated into QCA year 3 Gymnastics unit. Ask children to do hops/jumps to spring from place to place. They should move small distances at first, gradually progressing to longer hops/jumps. Discuss the force with which their feet push from the floor each time they hop/jump – ask whether short or longer hops/jumps need more force. The ideas will also help reinforce the understanding of the terms forces, pushes and pulls, attract and repel, spring.

Worksheet 2 is a wordsearch page. This page helps to reinforce knowledge of materials and the magnetic properties of iron and steel.

Worksheet 3 contains instructional text showing appropriate use of bullet points and numbers. This is also ideal for demonstrating that instructions begin with verbs. The pictures needed to complete the activity are provided on Worksheet 4.

Worksheet 5 is suitable for OHP use. It contains an ideal activity for an 'introduction of packaging' unit by setting the challenge of producing a pet carrier for a 'pulling pet' that has been created from Worksheet 4. Emphasise comfort of pet when travelling: The pet should be able to stand comfortably and be able to turn round in order to enter and leave the carrier facing forward. The pet should also be able to breathe! If possible show children examples/pictures of pet carriers. Children should also have had some experience of nets of shapes. This task enables you to provide materials and adhesives readily available in the classroom.

Worksheet 6 provides investigations involving measuring in standard units.

History – If you are studying the Vikings it is worth noting that they were the first to make practical use of magnets to make a simple compass aid for navigation.

Follow the leader

Read the instructions to learn how to play a new game in PE.

Work in pairs – one to lead and one to follow.

Player One is the leader and moves within the borders of a mat or a small area.

Player Two is the follower and copies the movements but always keeps a small distance away, as if being **repelled** by an invisible force.

Make up a simple sequence of movements using legs, arms and other body parts … or you could just use your whole body.

Take it in turns to be the leader or the follower.

If you are pleased with your sequence you could make up a series of simple diagrams to enable other pairs to follow it.

Name: Date:

Materials wordsearch

The words in the box can all be found in the wordsearch tin.

Shade each word as you find it.

When you have found the words, write them in the correct place at the bottom of the page.

The words might be written horizontally ⟶ , vertically ↓ or diagonally. ↘

WORD BANK

copper	wood	gold
silver	iron	steel
aluminium	brick	ice
cotton	paper	plastic

```
q c w e p l a s t i c
g o l d r w c t m y n
u p b i v o o c p x l
z p k a a j t o s h d
g e f q l z t w d x e
c r r v u t o b y n u
m i a p m s n m d s y
j t k m i r p x q i m
w i r o n d e i p l r
p p b h i b e p c v v
q a h j u p r t b e o
c p x n m t k i w r p
m e t o e p w p c v m
s r d l i p c s y k b
t s t e e l d t z o v
```

Metal   Non-metal

_____ _____ Which two items would
be attracted to a magnet?

_____ _____

_____ _____ _ _ _ _ and

_____ _____

_____ _____ _ _ _ _ _

_____ _____

Name: Date:

'Pulling pets'

Follow the instructions carefully to make a pulling pet.

<u>You will need:</u>

● card 'pet' shapes (front and back)

● 1 spring

● 2 split pins (Note: these are sharp so handle them with care)

● colouring pens/pencils

● 15cm length of cotton or string

● optional decorative items, e.g. sequins for eyes

<u>Instructions:</u>

● Choose one of the pet shapes on Worksheet 4, or draw your own in the blank rectangles.

● Cut out the front and back of your pet.

● Colour your pet and add any decorations.

● Score along the dotted lines and fold the stands beneath the feet of your pet. The front 'stand' must be folded towards the back of your pet and the back 'stand' must be folded towards the front.

● Carefully push the split pins through the centre of your front and back pieces to attach the spring to your pet.

● Tie your cotton/string to the split pin through the front of your pet. Use it as a 'lead' to pull your pet along.

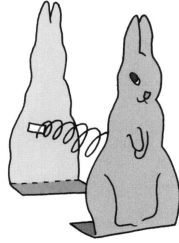

● Investigate your spring.

Name: | Date:

'Pulling pets'

 Here are the 'pulling pets' templates.

 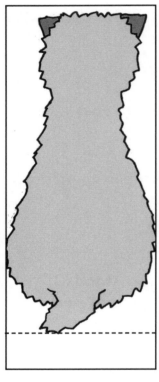 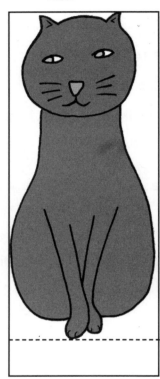 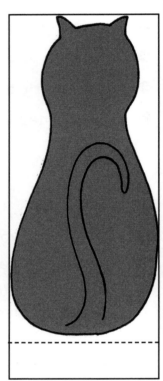

 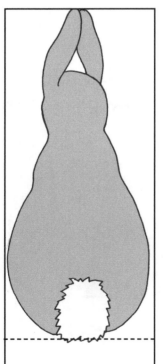  

Name: Date:

Make a Pet Carrier for your Pulling Pet

- Your pet is going on a journey.
- You must make a carrier to keep it comfortable and safe.

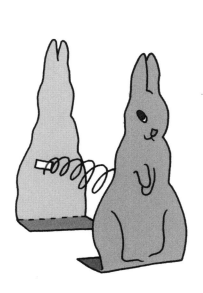

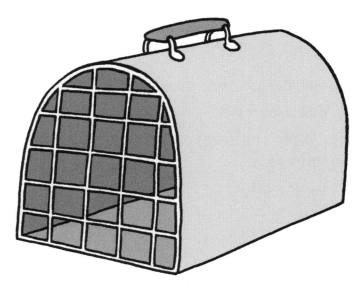

This is one type of pet carrier. Have you ever seen any others? Try to think of the best type for your pet.

Things to think about!

- How will your pet get in and out of its carrier?
- Make sure your pet can breathe.
- How will you carry the pet carrier?
- Do you want your pet to be able to see out?
- You can use any of the materials your teacher has provided for you.

Name: Date:

'Pulling Pets' Investigations

You will need:

- one 'pulling pet'
- ruler marked in centimetres
- weights (1gm to 5gm weights)

Place your pet so that the front of the pet is by the 0cm point on your ruler.

Gently pull your pet.

How far does the front of the pet move before the spring makes the back of the pet move?

Record your result.

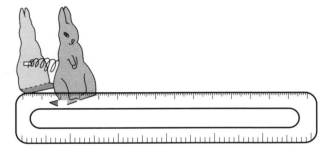

Now attach a 1gm weight to the back of your pet, using sticky tape.

Repeat the test.

Record your result.

Repeat the test several times using different weights.

Record your results.

Make a chart showing your results.

What did you find out?

weight added	distance pulled before movement
0	
1gm	
2gm	
3gm	

Can you think of other ways of using your pet to investigate forces?

Name:

Date:

Name:

Date:

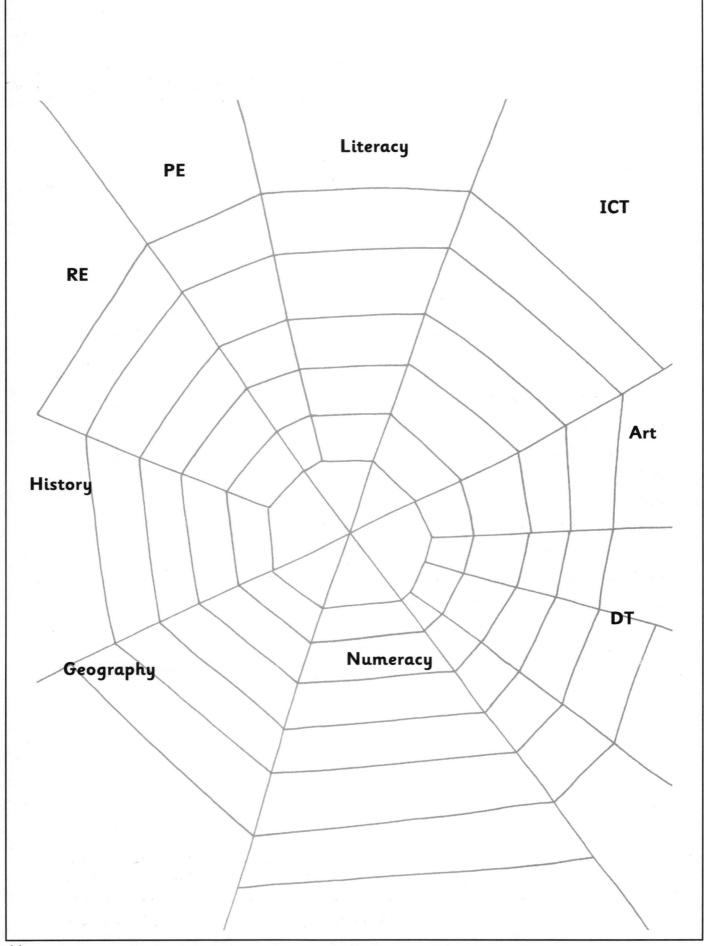

Literacy

PE

ICT

RE

Art

History

DT

Geography

Numeracy